Druids

- 3. VOYAGE OF DISCOVERY -

STORY
JEAN-LUC ISTIN & THIERRY JIGOUREL

ARTWORK
JACQUES LAMONTAGNE

ENGLISH ADAPTATION
LANNIG TRESELZH

DALEN

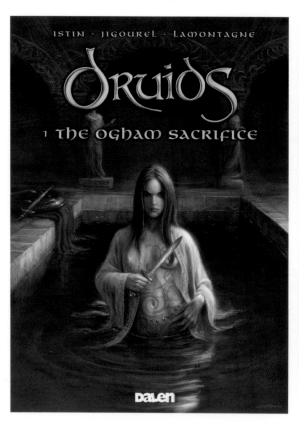

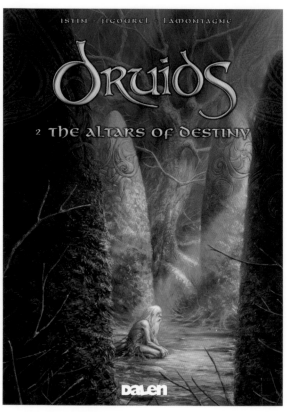

THE MYSTERY SO FAR:
THE OGHAM SACRIFICE
AND
THE ALTARS OF DESTINY

THE BEGINNING WAS...

...THE END.

I WAS REBORN, BENEATH THE WAVES.

MYSTERIOUS LIGHTS LIT THE DEPTHS.

AS I WAS GREETED BY MAIDENS FROM THE ABYSS, MY FEARS DISSOLVED IN THE ENVELOPING COLD OF THE WATER.

ENTRANCED BY THEIR STRANGE BEAUTY, I SLOWLY SANK INTO THE DARK OCEAN'S WOMB FROM WHENCE I WOULD BE BORN ANEW.

THEIR HAUNTING SONG, GIVEN BY THE GODS, CALMED ALL OF MY WORRIES, A SONG TO CARRY MY MORTAL SOUL FROM THIS WORLD TO THE NEXT.

FACING MY DEATH AND REBIRTH, MY GAZE TURNED UPWARDS TO A VOICE FROM MY PAST...

TARAN...

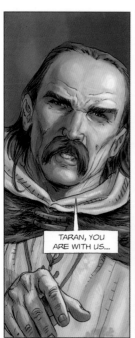

TARAN, YOU ARE WITH US...

MASTER.

I AM GLAD TO FIND YOU BETTER, FOR NOW WE ARE SAFE AFTER AN EASY CROSSING TO MÔN.

BROTHER MECHELL FROM THIS ISLE BROUGHT YOU BACK FROM THE CLUTCHES OF DEATH.

DON'T GET UP, YOU NEED TO REST.

WHAT PASSED TODAY WILL SURELY CHANGE YOUR LIFE.

YOU WERE TAKEN BY DEATH, BUT CAME BACK TO US HAVING GLIMPSED THE OTHER SIDE.

YOU ARE NOW A FULLY ORDAINED DRUID.

SLEEP, TARAN.

DID HE AWAKEN?

YES...

YOUR HEALING POWERS ARE IMMENSE. TARAN OWES YOU HIS LIFE.

MY DESIRE TO HEAL IS PART OF MY BEING...

THIS ISLE WAS ONCE A SANCTUARY FOR THE OLD FAITH. COUNTLESS DRUIDS WERE INSTRUCTED HERE, MANY IN THE ART OF HEALING.

HAD ROME NOT OVERRUN THIS ISLAND AND DESECRATED OUR ANCIENT GROVES, WE MIGHT ALL HAVE BECOME DRUIDS.

I KNOW YOU WILL KEEP THESE WORDS IN YOUR CONFIDENCE... OUR NEW FAITH HAS RETAINED MANY OF THE OLD WAYS, INCLUDING THE KNOWLEDGE OF HEALING...

I MUST CONFESS THAT ON OCCASION I GIVE PRAISE TO THE ANCIENT GODS INSTEAD OF TO THE LORD OUR SAVIOUR.

YOU ARE SURELY NOW AWARE OF THE FORCES HERE WHICH REVEAL THE OTHERWORLD.

WE MUST, HOWEVER, DEPART.

REMAIN HERE FOR AS LONG AS YOU PLEASE. MANY OF US STILL EMBRACE THE OLD FAITH.

WE CANNOT STAY MUCH LONGER. WE HAVE A LONG JOURNEY AHEAD OF US.

COMPANIONS OF OURS WILL SOON BE ARRIVING, MONKS SUCH AS YOURSELF. ONCE TARAN IS WELL, WE WILL LEAVE.

THIS JOURNEY MUST BE IMPORTANT.

IT IS. WE NEED TO SHOW THAT DRUIDS ARE NOT RESPONSIBLE FOR THE MANY VICIOUS MURDERS OF WHICH THEY ARE ACCUSED.

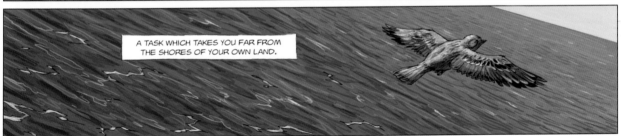

A TASK WHICH TAKES YOU FAR FROM THE SHORES OF YOUR OWN LAND.

THIS IS A VENTURE RIDDLED WITH COMPLEXITIES.

I DESPISE THESE IRISH MERCENARIES.

I PREFER THEM TO THOSE SAXON HOUNDS.

A PROMISE OF A HEALTHY REWARD, REGULAR GRATUITIES AND A SUBSTANTIAL ADVANCE HAS ENSURED THEY WILL LAY DOWN THEIR LIVES FOR US. INDEED, WE CANNOT DO WITHOUT THEM.

BUT THEY ARE UNDOUBTEDLY USEFUL. SURROUNDED BY DANGERS, THEIR PRESENCE KEEPS MOST RAIDERS FROM ATTACKING US.

THE SPEAR WAS LOST...

YES, BUT ITS LOSS COULD THREATEN THE ORDER.

IT IS NOW FAR FROM THE REACH OF ALL.

THAT DESPICABLE DRUID MUST DIE. IT IS HE WHO IS TO BLAME.

GWYNLAN? DON'T BE SUCH A FOOL! GURVAN ALONE IS TO BLAME. HE WAS RASH IN DISMISSING THE SPEAR'S IMPORTANCE TO KER-IS. HAD HE LISTENED TO ME, KER-IS WOULD NOW BE IN OUR HANDS.

WE CANNOT LOSE SIGHT OF OUR GOAL AGAIN. THE CAULDRON OF DESTINY MUST BECOME OURS – THE LORD DEMANDS IT!

WE ARE TOLD THE DRUID'S PUPIL IS GRAVELY ILL.

LET US SAIL AT ONCE TO THE ISLE OF AILBE...

THAT IS A PITY.

BECAUSE WE DO NOT YET KNOW THE EXACT COURSE TO FOLLOW.

BUT GWYNLAN DOES – OR, HE HAS A BETTER IDEA THAN WE DO. WHILE HE CAN SERVE US, HE LIVES.

THE DAYS ON MÔN WERE SLOW TO PASS, BUT MY HEALING WAS RAPID.

MAWDEZ AND THE BROTHERS JOINED US IN DUE COURSE...

THEY WERE ASTOUNDED AT HOW QUICKLY I HAD RECOVERED.

MY ACQUAINTANCE WITH MECHELL BECAME DEEPER. HIS CALM TEMPERAMENT REFLECTED A QUIET DISPOSITION. HE TAUGHT ME MUCH, ENRICHING MY KNOWLEDGE OF HEALING.

MY SOUL MATURED AS A CONSEQUENCE. I BECAME LESS WARY AND FAR MORE CONFIDENT IN MY SKILLS. THE REASON FOR MY EXISTENCE AND PURPOSE WAS NOW EVIDENT. I CAST ASIDE ANY FRIVOLOUS CURIOSITY.

I BECAME THE MAN I WAS MEANT TO BE.

HENCEFORTH I WOULD SERVE OTHERS, HEALING PHYSICAL AS WELL AS SPIRITUAL WOUNDS.

AS THE GODS CONSIDERED MY TRANSFORMATION, I WAS SOON TO BE TESTED...

TARAN, HURRY!

COME QUICKLY! WE NEED YOU!

WHAT HAPPENED?

WE DON'T KNOW EXACTLY WHAT HAPPENED, BUT WE FOUND HIM SHOT WITH AN ARROW.

PUT HIM TO LIE FACE DOWN!...

AND QUICKLY FETCH BROTHER MECHELL.

HE HAS SAILED TO THE MAINLAND AND WON'T RETURN UNTIL TOMORROW.

IN THAT CASE, WE HAVE TO PROCEED WITHOUT HIM.

I WAS BEING TESTED BY THE GODS.

DESPITE BEING TESTED, I KNEW THIS WAS MY VOCATION – THE BOY'S WOUND WAS GRAVE.

CAN I BE OF HELP?

ALL IS WELL. THE BOY WILL SOON COME TO.

HE'S AWAKE!

SAY, HOW WERE YOU WOUNDED?

I... I...

YES?

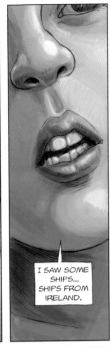

I SAW SOME SHIPS... SHIPS FROM IRELAND.

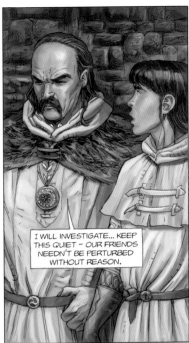

I WILL INVESTIGATE... KEEP THIS QUIET – OUR FRIENDS NEEDN'T BE PERTURBED WITHOUT REASON.

YOU FOOLS!

HE SAW US!

THAT WOULD NOT HAVE HAPPENED IF YOU HAD REMAINED ABOARD YOUR SHIPS AS I INSTRUCTED.

DON'T FRET. I SHOT HIM IN THE BACK WITH AN ARROW TO SEE HIM OFF TO HELL.

DEAD OR ALIVE, IF HE IS FOUND WITH OUR ARROW IN HIS BACK, IT WON'T BE LONG BEFORE OUR MISSION IS UNCOVERED.

10

IS AN ATTACK IMMINENT?

YES, AND LED BY MEN CLOTHED IN BLACK...

IF THEY WANTED TO ATTACK, THEY WOULD ALREADY HAVE DONE SO. I VENTURE THAT THESE MEN ARE ON THE SAME QUEST AS US. WE ARE MOST LIKELY A STEP OR TWO AHEAD OF THEM... AND THAT'S WHY THEY'RE WATCHING US.

WHO ARE THEY?

ALL I KNOW IS THAT THEY OBSERVE OF ONE OF THE ANCIENT GODS, ESUS, AND ARE LOYAL TO WHAT REMAINS OF AN OLD CHRISTIAN ORDER, THE HOLY VENGEANCE. THEY SEEK THE TREASURES OF THE BRITONS AND WON'T REFRAIN FROM BLOODSHED TO ACHIEVE THEIR GOAL.

THEY ARE THE ONES RESPONSIBLE FOR THE KILLING OF MONKS IN BRITTANY, AND FOR PLACING THE BLAME AT THE FEET OF THE DRUIDS.

FORGIVE ME, GWYNLAN, BUT WHAT IF THE DRUIDS ARE IN FACT GUILTY?

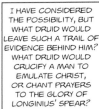

I HAVE CONSIDERED THE POSSIBILITY, BUT WHAT DRUID WOULD LEAVE SUCH A TRAIL OF EVIDENCE BEHIND HIM? WHAT DRUID WOULD CRUCIFY A MAN TO EMULATE CHRIST, OR CHANT PRAYERS TO THE GLORY OF LONGINIUS' SPEAR?

I AGREE... BUT NO CHRISTIAN WOULD PRAISE ESUS. CONSEQUENTLY, THOSE RESPONSIBLE CANNOT BE CHRISTIANS EITHER.

THE DISCIPLES OF ESUS.

TARAN, AS YOU ARE NOW IN GOOD HEALTH, WE MUST LEAVE MÔN.

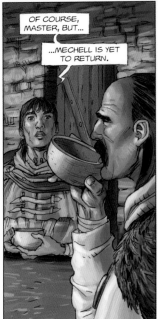

OF COURSE, MASTER, BUT...

...MECHELL IS YET TO RETURN.

WE CAN'T WAIT FOR HIM. WE HAVE TO TAKE ADVANTAGE OF THE CURRENT WIND FROM THE SOUTH.

BEFORE LONG, MÔN WAS FAR BEHIND US. MECHELL WOULD SOON RETURN; I HAD LEFT HIM A MESSAGE THAT I WOULD REVISIT IN DUE COURSE TO CONTINUE MY LEARNING.

BEFORE LONG, THE SUN SET ON THE FIRST DAY OF OUR VOYAGE.

HOW IS IT THAT OUR ENEMIES ARE ON OUR TAIL?

KEEP YOUR VOICE DOWN, TARAN!

AS THEY ARE CLOSE ON OUR HEELS, THERE MUST BE A TRAITOR IN OUR MIDST.

THAT NIGHT AT THE GIANT'S DANCE, I SAW FEET LEAVING OUR CAMP. WHEN I AWOKE, I SAW MAWDEZ. HE SAID HE'D BEEN TO ANSWER THE CALL OF NATURE.

MAWDEZ?

CAN WE TRUST HIM?

I'M SURE WE CAN, BUT WE MUST BE CAUTIOUS.

SUDDENLY, WE WERE ENGULFED IN MIST...

FAR TOO SUDDENLY.

BROTHER ILLTUD?

THE WATER IS SHALLOW HERE.

WE ARE CLOSE TO SHORE... AND WE SHOULD LAND. TRYING TO CONTINUE OUR VOYAGE IN THIS WEATHER IS DANGEROUS.

OUR BOAT QUIETLY BEACHED ON ONE OF THE HEBRIDEAN ISLANDS.

WE COULD SMELL THE SCENT OF GRASSES AND FLOWERING PLANTS CARRIED BY THE GENTLE BREEZE OF THE MISTY GLOOM.

BUT WE WERE ALL BUT BLIND TO ANY GREENERY AND COLOUR...

TO SAVE US FROM DISAPPEARING INTO THE MIST, WE SECURED OURSELVES TO ONE ANOTHER AS WE PROCEEDED ON FOOT.

WHAT EXACTLY ARE WE LOOKING FOR?

WHAT AN INANE QUESTION, BROTHER ILLTUD.

WE'RE LOOKING FOR A REFUGE UNTIL THE MIST CLEARS.

WHAT ELSE WOULD WE BE LOOKING FOR?

13

WE SHOULD BE FINE HERE UNTIL THE MIST HAS GONE.

GWYNLAN, BROTHER ILLTUD IS NOT HERE.

LOOK AT THE ROPE.

SEVERED BY A CLEAN CUT!

THEY HAVE FOUND US.

WHO?

THE PICTS, THE MOST MERCILESS TRIBE IN THE WHOLE OF BRITAIN. THE ROMANS WERE IN SUCH AWE OF THE PICTS AND THE TRIBES OF THE NORTH THAT THEY BUILT WALLS TO KEEP THEM FROM THE SOUTH OF THE ISLAND.

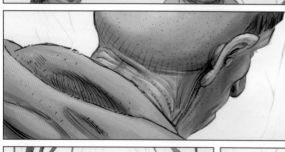

THE PICTS PAINT THEIR BODIES WITH PATTERNS OF BLUE WOAD – THEY ARE WARY FROM RECENT INCURSIONS INTO THEIR LANDS BY THE GAELS OF IRELAND.

WE MUST FIND BROTHER ILLTUD.

ALAS, YOUR EFFORTS WOULD BE IN VAIN.

GWYNLAN, BROTHER PEDIG AND MYSELF WILL RETURN ALONG THE PATH. WE DO NOT KNOW THAT THE PICTS ARE THE CAUSE OF BROTHER ILLTUD'S DISAPPEARANCE.

DON'T, MAWDEZ!

MASTER!

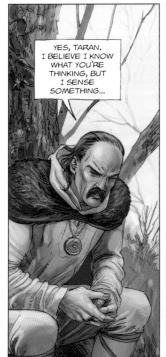

YES, TARAN. I BELIEVE I KNOW WHAT YOU'RE THINKING, BUT I SENSE SOMETHING...

...I SENSE WE ARE BEING WATCHED.

WE HAD BEST REMAIN HERE FOR THE TIME BEING.

ILLTUD'S FOOTPRINTS END HERE.

DID HE VANISH INTO THIN AIR?

NO... THERE ARE OTHER PRINTS AS WELL... BARE FEET.

HMFF!

WHAT...? PEDIG? WHERE ARE YOU?

HOLY MOTHER OF GOD!

AAAAAAARGH!!!

LET HIM GO!

YOU MAY ENGAGE IN COMBAT WITH BRIDEI, MY FRIEND...

...BUT YOU WILL PAY WITH YOUR LIFE.

I WILL PAY THAT PRICE IF NEED BE, I DO NOT FEAR DEATH.

HO! HO! HO! HO!

I KNOW. A DRUID DOES NOT FLEE FROM HIS END.

WELCOME TO THE HEBRIDES, BROTHER. THE YOUNG DRUID IS FINE... NO MORE THAN A BUMP TO HIS HEAD.

YOUR OTHER COMPANIONS ARE IN OUR VILLAGE. FOLLOW ME.

YOU MUST FORGIVE ME... I DID NOT KNOW THE CHRISTIANS WERE ACCOMPANIED BY TWO DRUIDS – OTHERWISE OUR WELCOME WOULD HAVE BEEN WARMER...

I SHOULD HAVE REALISED... WE HAVE BEEN EXPECTING YOU FOR A LONG WHILE.

BEFORE THE MOON WAS HIGH IN THE NIGHT SKY, THE FEAST DREW TO A CLOSE. AS OUR COMPANIONS FELL ASLEEP, TALORGAN INSISTED ON TAKING US FAR FROM THE WORLD'S PRYING EYES. HE LED US TO HIS CHAMBER DEEP INSIDE A MYSTERIOUS CAVE...

THROUGHOUT THE FEAST, GWYNLAN, I COULD SENSE YOU WANTED TO ASK ME SOMETHING.

TELL ME, WHAT IS ON YOUR MIND?

TALORGAN, ON OUR WAY TO YOUR VILLAGE, YOU SAID THE PICTS WERE EXPECTING US.

I DID... IT WAS TOLD THAT YOU WOULD COME AND THAT WHAT IS DEAR TO US WOULD ALSO ASSIST YOU.

ASSIST US?

IT IS NOT BY CHANCE THAT YOU ARE HERE...

WHAT DO YOU SEEK?

THE CAULDRON OF REBIRTH.

I SEE.

THE PATH TO THE CAULDRON HAS BROUGHT YOU HERE.

TAKE THIS CUP AND DRINK...

DRINK.

LOOK...

SEE...

THE CAULDRON CAME TO GWYNLAN'S EYES...

...HE SAW THE PICTS TAKE THE CAULDRON FAR FROM THE HEBRIDES.

THEN HIS EYES SAW NORTHMEN IN THEIR LONGSHIPS...

...AND THEIR WARRIORS PILLAGING THE VILLAGE...

...TO STEAL THE STONE OF DESTINY...

...AND TAKE IT FAR AWAY FROM THE HEBRIDES.

THAT IS THE SAD STORY OF MY PEOPLE, GWYNLAN.

DEATH AND TRIBULATION HAVE RAVAGED OUR LAND SINCE WE LOST THE STONE OF DESTINY.

TO WHERE WAS THE STONE TAKEN?

ACCORDING TO BRENDAN, A YOUNG AND COURAGEOUS FOLLOWER OF CHRIST, IT WOULD HAVE BEEN TAKEN TO THE ISLE OF AILBE...

WHICH MEANS THEY TOOK THE SAME ROUTE AS THE CAULDRON.

AS I SAID, WHAT IS DEAR TO US WOULD ALSO ASSIST YOU.

MY BRAVEST WARRIORS WILL ACCOMPANY YOU TO AILBE. WE MUST RETRIEVE THE STONE, AND NEED YOUR HELP TO DO SO.

MY HELP?

YES, THIS IS OUR DEAL. WE WILL HELP YOU REACH AILBE AND YOU WILL BRING US THE STONE.

MY MASTER ACCEPTED THE DEAL. BEFORE LONG, WE SET SAIL IN A MIGHTY FLEET.

GWENOLÉ...

GWENOLÉ...

WHO?

BLESSED VIRGIN MARY!

I HAVE A TASK FOR YOU, BROTHER GWENOLÉ.

I AM YOUR FAITHFUL SERVANT, OH MOTHER OF GOD.

I AM HERE TO OBEY.

SAVE THE DRUIDS.

MY LADY...

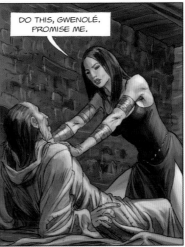

DO THIS, GWENOLÉ. PROMISE ME.

NO, DAHUD... DON'T!

I HAVE LONGED FOR YOU SINCE OUR FIRST ENCOUNTER, GWENOLÉ... MY FLESH, MY PASSION ARE YOURS...

A VISION FROM HELL!

WHY IS MY MIND DISINTEGRATING?

WHAT LEADS ME TO THESE DESIRES?

LORD, I NO LONGER HAVE THE RIGHT TO LIVE.

I HAVE BETRAYED THEE.

HEAVENLY FATHER, FORGIVE ME.

BROTHER GWENOLÉ.

YES?

I BRING GOOD NEWS. THOSE RESPONSIBLE FOR KILLING OUR MONKS HAVE BEEN DETAINED.

MAY THEY BURN IN THE FIRES OF HELL! HALLELUJAH!

MANY DAYS LATER, OUR VOYAGE REACHED ITS END...

...ON THE BEACHES OF THE ISLES OF SHEEP. THE PREVIOUS NIGHTS HAD BEEN LONG, WITH NO OPPORTUNITY TO REST OR SLEEP.

WE RECEIVED AN UNEXPECTED AND WARM WELCOME BY THE SHORE.

THERE, PAUSING ON THEIR OWN LONG VOYAGE, WE MET A MONK AND HIS COMPANIONS.

WHO ARE THESE STRANGE MARINERS?

ARMORICAN DRUIDS, MEN OF THE PICTS, AND MONKS FROM THE BRITISH CHURCH, ALL TOGETHER! HOW COULD THIS BE?!

WHOEVER YOU ARE, BRAVE SAILORS, I AM BRENDAN OF IRELAND. WELCOME!

BRENDAN! THANK THE LORD FOR THIS FORTUITOUS AND FORTUNATE ENCOUNTER.

INDEED, THE LORD BE PRAISED, BROTHER. BUT HOW DID FATE BRING YOUR COMPANY TOGETHER?

THE YOUNG MONK'S WELCOME WAS SINCERE. BRENDAN'S FAME HAD ALREADY SPREAD FROM IRELAND TO BRITAIN WHERE HE HAD WON THE RESPECT OF THE PICTS.

I HOPE YOU APPRECIATE LONG STORIES...

THE LONGER THE BETTER!

MASTER, WHO IS THAT YOUNG MAN?

HE IS BRENDAN, ONE OF IRELAND'S MOST ILLUSTRIOUS MONKS. HE IS RENOWNED FAR AND WIDE. IT IS SAID THAT HE HAS CROSSED THE OCEANS AND DISCOVERED THE LANDS OF OUR LEGENDS.

I HAVE LONG DREAMED OF MEETING YOU AND TO SHARE TALES OF EVANGELISING IN DISTANT LANDS. I HAVE READ MANY ACCOUNTS OF YOUR VOYAGE TO THE LAND OF THE NORTHMEN.

AND WE MEET AT THIS FATEFUL MOMENT IN MY LIFE!

FATEFUL MOMENT?

WITH THE LORD'S GUIDING WIND BEHIND US, WE ARE ABOUT TO SET SAIL TO SEEK THE FABLED LAND OF NA N'OG!

HAVE YOU HEARD THE STORIES OF THE VOYAGE OF BRÂN?

SOME, YES.

WELL, BRÂN SPOKE OF A LAND FAR TO THE WEST, BEYOND THE BOUNDS OF OUR KNOWLEDGE, A LAND HE CALLED TIR NA N'OG, THE LAND OF ETERNAL YOUTH...

BUT THAT'S NOTHING MORE THAN A FABLE!

MAYBE, BUT THERE IS A GRAIN OF TRUTH IN THE LEGEND. OUR MISSION IS TO UNCOVER THAT TRUTH. THERE IS UNDOUBTEDLY ANOTHER LAND BEYOND THE WESTERN OCEAN... SO OFTEN REFERRED TO BY OUR FOREFATHERS AS THE LAND OF YOUTH.

I HAVE ALSO HEARD OF THE LAND WHICH CAN ONLY BE REACHED BY A FROZEN PATH OF WHITE...

WHAT BROUGHT YOU HERE?

...A VOYAGE TO THE ISLE OF AILBE.

THE LORD IS MERCIFUL... I KNOW THE WAY TO AILBE!

AILBE IS ALSO ON OUR ROUTE. WE'LL SET SAIL TOMORROW.

BRENDAN...
YOU AGAIN.

WHAT WILL YOU DO ON THE ISLE OF AILBE?

SHOULD WE TELL HIM, GWYNLAN?

OF COURSE WE SHOULD... OTHERWISE HOW WILL HE KNOW OUR INTENTIONS?

WHAT EXACTLY DO YOU INTEND? THE MYSTERY HAS HEIGHTENED MY CURIOSITY!

WE INTEND TO RECOVER THE PICTS' SACRED STONE FROM THE NORTHMEN.

THE STONE KEPT IN THE MIDDLE OF THEIR SETTLEMENT?

I KNOW THESE NORTHMEN.

AND YOU WILL THEREFORE UNDERSTAND WHY WE CANNOT REVEAL OUR INTENTIONS TO THEM. WE CANNOT ALLOW YOU TO SEE THE NORTHMEN WHILE WE SEEK THE STONE.

I APPRECIATE YOUR POSITION, BUT WHAT PURPOSE IS THERE TO THIS QUEST? WHY IS THE STONE SO IMPORTANT?

THE STONE IS PRECIOUS TO THE PICTS. ITS RETRIEVAL IS IN RECOMPENSE FOR THEIR HELP ON OUR JOURNEY. THIS IS THE ROUTE FOLLOWED BY THE PICTS WHEN THEY TOOK THE CAULDRON OF REBIRTH TO SAFETY.

THE CAULDRON OF REBIRTH? DOES IT REALLY EXIST?

INDEED IT DOES... AND IT SEEMS IT NOW RESIDES ON THE ISLE OF AILBE.

IT IS A DESCENT INTO A VERY UNCHRISTIAN PIT, MY FRIEND.

THIS IS TOO MUCH FOR ME. I MUST TAKE MY LEAVE...

BROTHER MAWDEZ...

YES?

BRENDAN MISTRUSTS ME... BUT I NEED DETAILS OF ALL HE KNOWS ABOUT THE NORTHMEN...

A TRUSTING BOND GREW BETWEEN BRENDAN AND MAWDEZ. THE IRISH MONK REVEALED HIS SOUL TO OUR FRIEND FROM ENEZ VRIAD. HE DISCLOSED ALL HE KNEW ABOUT THE NORTHMEN, SO MUCH SO THAT MAWDEZ BECAME INTIMATELY FAMILIAR WITH THE ISLAND WE WERE APPROACHING.

AS ADVISED BY BRENDAN, WE LANDED ON AILBE AT NIGHT IN A BAY SURROUNDED BY HIGH CLIFFS.

QUIET, EVERYONE...

OUR NOISE WILL CARRY...

WE'RE FROZEN TO THE BONE...

IN A NEARBY CAVE WE CAN LIGHT A FIRE WITHOUT DRAWING ATTENTION.

HURRY! THIS IS SUCH AN UNHOLY PLACE!

HERE IT IS... THE CAVE WILL LEAD US TO THE HEART OF THE ISLAND.

THIS IS MUCH BETTER! LET'S LIGHT OUR TORCHES!

I APOLOGISE FOR IMPOSING ON YOU THIS WAY, BRENDAN.

ALTHOUGH I WAS ONCE THE NORTHMEN'S PRISONER, I FEEL UNEASY ABOUT THIS SITUATION. THIS ENTERPRISE WILL SOON BE OVER, OR SO YOU SAID.

I AM SURE IT WILL BE.

THEN LET US PRAY THAT I MAY GUIDE YOU TO THE STONE OF DESTINY.

HE'S GOING TO SOUND HIS HORN!

ARGH!

WHAT THE...?

TCHOP

THANK YOU, GWYNLAN.

WE MUST HURRY. WHEN THE NORTHMEN REALISE ONE OF THEIR BAND HAS DISAPPEARED, THEY WILL BE OUT SEARCHING FOR HIM — AND THEN THEY'RE BOUND TO FIND OUR SHIPS.

I'VE WANDERED THE LENGTH AND BREADTH OF THESE CAVES.

DIDN'T YOU LOSE YOUR WAY?

I CUT SIGNS IN THE ROCK TO MARK MY WAY...

THE SIGN OF THE LORD.

TARAN!

ONE OF THE MEN WAS INJURED AS HE LEFT THE SHIP.

I WILL COME IMMEDIATELY.

YOU ARE PROFICIENT AT HEALING!

MY EXCELLENT TEACHER WAS LIKE YOU, A MONK.

AS I SEE THIS YOUNG MAN PRACTISE HIS SKILL I AM CONVINCED – DESPITE ALL OUR TEACHINGS – WE SHOULD SHARE OUR KNOWLEDGE.

I ABSOLUTELY AGREE...

YOU BLIND FOOLS! CAN'T YOU SEE THE DIFFERENCE BETWEEN GOOD AND EVIL?

TEMPER YOUR WORDS, BROTHER!

TEMPER MY WORDS, BROTHER MAWDEZ, AS I SEE YOU IN ALLIANCE WITH PAGANS, TAKING THE LORD'S NAME IN VAIN?!

IN VAIN, I SAY!

THESE PAGANS AREN'T EVEN DESERVING OF HELL'S ETERNAL FLAMES!

FLAP

AARGH!

LET'S GIVE THEM A REASON TO BE WARY...

...AFTER WE RETURN TO THE CAVE.

BRENDAN IS AWARE OF OUR INTENTIONS, BUT HE WISHES TO AVOID A BLOODY END TO OUR ONSLAUGHT. HE KNOWS THE NORTHMEN BETTER THAN WE DO, BUT DESPITE OUR RIGHTEOUS CAUSE HE FEELS HE IS BETRAYING THEM.

IT'S A DILEMMA FOR HIM.

INDEED!

CAN WE TRUST HIM?

DO WE HAVE A CHOICE?

NO.

BUT THE STONE OF DESTINY HAS NOTHING TO DO WITH US, GWYNLAN.

I TRUST TALORGAN ENTIRELY.

MORE THAN I DO...

HIS REASONS ARE CLEAR ENOUGH. THE CAULDRON – OR AT LEAST THE PATH TOWARDS IT – IS ON THIS ISLAND.

MAYBE SO... BUT HELPING THE PICTS WILL INCUR THE WRATH OF THE NORTHMEN.

I HAVE NO ENMITY TOWARDS THE NORTHMEN. BUT I HAVE GIVEN MY PLEDGE TO THE PICTS. I FEEL IT IN MY BONES THAT WE'RE GETTING CLOSER TO THE CAULDRON.

VERY WELL, IF YOU INSIST.

OUR ENCOUNTER WITH BRENDAN, BE THAT BY DIVINE INTERVENTION OR BY PURE CHANCE, WAS MOST FORTUNATE.

BY HIS PREVIOUS WANDERINGS THROUGH THESE GALLERIES, BRENDAN HAD PUT THE VARIOUS TRAILS TO WRITING AND TO MEMORY.

HE TOOK US THROUGH THESE UNDERGROUND TUNNELS – GWYNLAN, ONUIST, NECHTAN AND MYSELF.

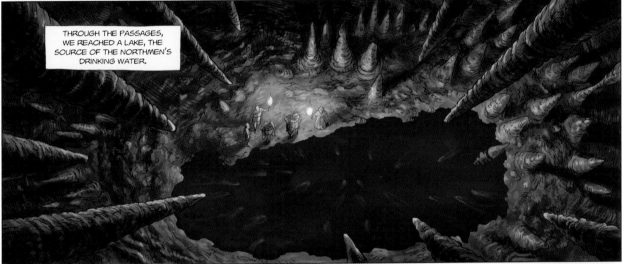

THROUGH THE PASSAGES, WE REACHED A LAKE, THE SOURCE OF THE NORTHMEN'S DRINKING WATER.

I HAVE NEVER FELT SO COLD, GWYNLAN.

WILL WE GET TO WARM OURSELVES AGAIN IN THE CAVE, BRENDAN?

35

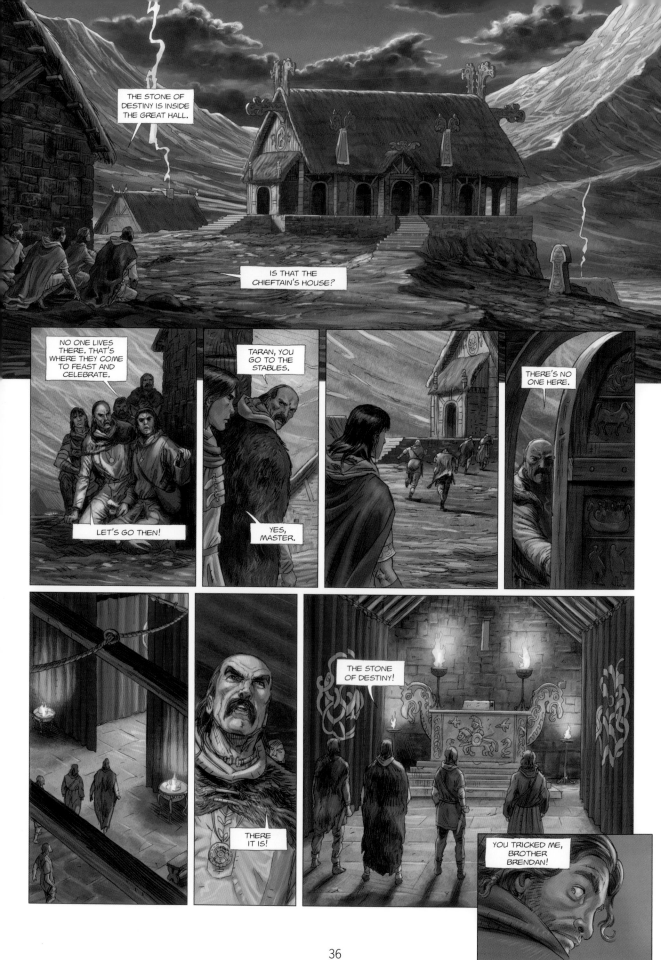

OLAF!

YOU OF ALL PEOPLE, BRENDAN. YOU WHO WERE ONCE AS A SON TO ME. DESPITE MY HAVING SPARED YOUR LIFE, YOUR GRATITUDE IS TREACHERY.

WE HAVE BOTH SHARED BETTER DAYS, OLAF.

DAYS THAT TURNED YOU TO BETRAYAL.

THOSE HERE WITH ME HAVE NO MALICE TOWARDS YOU.

NO MALICE, BUT SKULKING INTO OUR VILLAGE UNDER THE COVER OF DARKNESS IN ORDER TO TAKE THE STONE OF DESTINY FROM US.

YOUR TREACHERY WAS REVEALED BY THOSE FAITHFUL TO ESUS.

GWYNLAN...

IT'S NOT YOUR STONE! IT WAS YOU WHO STOLE IT FROM US!

ACCORDING TO OUR LAWS, IT IS NOW OURS! YOU WILL NEVER TAKE IT FROM US... NEVER!

PLEASE, OLAF, GIVE THEM THE STONE BEFORE ANY BLOODSHED. THE CAULDRON IS NOTHING BUT A PAGAN RELIC.

THE ONLY BLOOD TO BE SHED WILL BE YOURS AND YOUR FRIENDS', TRAITOR!

TAKE THEM TO THE ROCK!

SUTRIG! TAKE TWELVE MEN TO THE PICTS' HIDEOUT, AND KILL THEM ALL!

OLAF.

AS AGREED, WE NOW WISH TO SEE THE STONE.

YES.

BE MY GUESTS! TAKE YOUR TIME.

ALL BUT TARAN HAVE BEEN CAPTURED.

BLOODSHED IS NOW INEVITABLE. THESE NORTHMEN ARE SO FOOLISH!

FOOLS WALKING BLINDLY TO THEIR DEATH.

BROTHER GWENOLÉ, IT GIVES ME PLEASURE TO WELCOME YOU TO DOMNONEA.

WAS YOUR JOURNEY HERE EASY?

IT WAS NOT, BROTHER GILDAS. THESE AWFUL KILLINGS PLAY ON MY MIND. I FIND THEM QUITE A NIGHTMARE.

THE DEATHS OF OUR MONKS ARE TRULY APPALLING, BUT THEY ARE NOW GONE. A PACK OF DRUIDS HAVE BEEN CAPTURED AND INTERROGATED. THEY CONFESSED TO EVERYTHING.

WHAT EVIDENCE IS THERE?

WITNESSES AND THE DRUIDS' OWN WORDS. WE NEED NO MORE!

WHAT ON GOD'S EARTH IS THAT FOUL STENCH?

LET ME MEET THE WITNESSES...

WHY, SO? THE MATTER IS NOW CLOSED. WHY BOTHER THEM FURTHER?

TO EASE MY WORRIES, BROTHER GILDAS. WHAT IF ONE OF THE PAGANS HAS EVADED CAPTURE? LET ME QUESTION THEM AGAIN TO ENSURE EVERYTHING SUPPORTS YOUR OWN CAREFUL ENDEAVOURS.

OF COURSE. I AM CONFIDENT OUR ENQUIRIES HAVE BEEN THOROUGH, BUT WE MAY INDEED HAVE MISSED SOMETHING.

SOMETHING MISSED BY THE WITNESSES, NO DOUBT.

THEY ARE HERE, EXAMINE THEM AS YOU WILL. BROTHER CADFAN WILL STAY TO ASSIST YOU.

THANK YOU, BROTHER GILDAS.

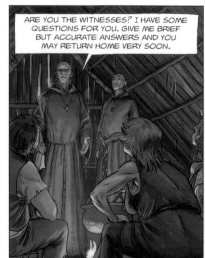

ARE YOU THE WITNESSES? I HAVE SOME QUESTIONS FOR YOU. GIVE ME BRIEF BUT ACCURATE ANSWERS AND YOU MAY RETURN HOME VERY SOON.

WE HAVE NO HOME. WE HAVE BEEN OFFERED SANCTUARY HERE FOR ALL TIME. THIS PLACE AND OUR FOOD IS GOOD. A PROMISE IS A PROMISE, AFTER ALL...

I WAS NOT AWARE OF THIS.

WHERE HAVE YOU BEEN?

HOW EXACTLY DID YOU COME TO KNOW THAT THESE DRUIDS WERE THE MURDERERS?

WHAT DO YOU MEAN?

HE! HE! HE! YOU FOOL! DON'T YOU UNDERSTAND THE PRIEST?

SHUT IT, OR I'LL THUMP YOU!

HA! HA! HA! HA!

DID YOU ACTUALLY SEE THE DRUIDS KILL, OR TRY TO KILL, A MONK?

UM...

DO YOU UNDERSTAND MY QUESTION?

THEY WERE WITNESSES TO A PLOT TO KILL!

BROTHER CADFAN, DO NOT ANSWER ON THEIR BEHALF!

THEY OBVIOUSLY DON'T UNDERSTAND YOU.

WHAT'S YOUR NAME?

CEDIG.

HOW DO YOU KNOW THESE DRUIDS, CEDIG?

THEY GAVE US FOOD AND SHELTER. WE HAD NOTHING... OUR HARVEST HAD FAILED, WE COULDN'T FEED OUR STOCK. WE WERE STARVING, LIVING ON CHARITY.

THESE DRUIDS HELPED YOU?

MOSTLY, YES, EXCEPT FOR THE LAST TIME. OUR BOY SAW THEM STUFFING THEIR FACES, BUT THEY GAVE US NOTHING!

I TOLD YOU THOSE DRUIDS HAD YOU IN THEIR FIST, CEDIG!

LISTEN, YOU OLD HAG, YOU WERE MORE THAN HAPPY TO SLEEP UNDER THEIR ROOF AND EAT THEIR FOOD!

WHAT DID YOU TELL THE BROTHERS?

THE TRUTH... THAT THE DRUIDS HATE CHRISTIANS! NO WONDER THEY WANTED TO KILL THE MONKS.

IS THAT ALL?

ISN'T THAT ENOUGH, BROTHER GWENOLÉ? DRUIDS WHO WANTED TO KILL CHRISTIANS!

I MYSELF HAVE OFTEN WANTED TO THROTTLE A FEW PAGANS, BUT I'VE NEVER DONE SO!

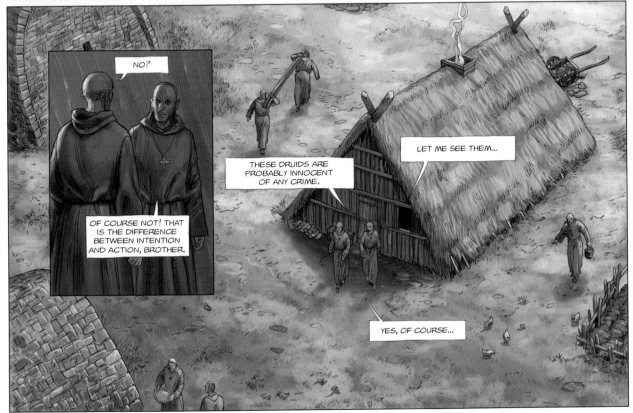

NO?

OF COURSE NOT! THAT IS THE DIFFERENCE BETWEEN INTENTION AND ACTION, BROTHER.

THESE DRUIDS ARE PROBABLY INNOCENT OF ANY CRIME.

LET ME SEE THEM...

YES, OF COURSE...

41

BOUAAH

BUT WHY DID YOU KILL INNOCENT MEN?

SUCH WORDS ARE FUTILE.

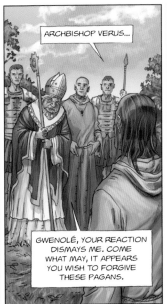

ARCHBISHOP VERUS...

GWENOLÉ, YOUR REACTION DISMAYS ME. COME WHAT MAY, IT APPEARS YOU WISH TO FORGIVE THESE PAGANS.

IS THAT THE CASE?

I WISH TO FIND NOTHING BUT THE TRUTH.

THE TRUTH? WHAT I SAY IS THE TRUTH! EVEN IF THESE DRUIDS DID NOT THEMSELVES MURDER OUR MONKS, THEY ARE GUILTY! GUILTY IN THE EYES OF OUR LORD.

I BELIEVED I COULD RELY ON YOU FOR ASSISTANCE. I WAS MISTAKEN.

THE PEOPLE ARE FRIGHTENED. GOD'S SERVANTS LIE DEAD AT THE HANDS OF PAGANS. MY DECISION WAS TO RID THE LAND OF THE REMNANTS OF THE DRUIDIC FAITH. THOSE WHO DENY OUR LORD FACE THE SEVEREST RETRIBUTION.

YOU CAN'T...

INSOLENCE!

MY AUTHORITY IS LAW IN ALL RESPECTS!

CONSIDER YOUR WORDS VERY CAREFULLY, BROTHER GWENOLÉ, LEST YOU FIND YOURSELF INCARCERATED AND LEFT TO ROT!

RETURN FORTHWITH TO YOUR MONASTERY, AND STAY THERE OUT OF MY SIGHT!

VENERABLE VERUS...

AS ALL HE HELD DEAR WAS WRENCHED AWAY, THIS WAS A TURNING POINT FOR GWENOLÉ.

THE PRICE OF A MAN'S SOUL BECAME CENTRAL TO THE BELIEFS OF LANDEVENEG'S ABBOT. HIS GOD WAS THE GOD OF LOVE AND FORGIVENESS, NOT ARCHBISHOP VERUS' GOD OF HATE AND REVENGE.

WAS IT DAHUD'S DEMISE THAT LED HIM TO THIS BELIEF?

GWENOLÉ HIMSELF WAS UNSURE. DAHUD CONFUSED HIM, A CONSTANT CONFLICT BETWEEN THIS AND THE OTHER WORLD – A BATTLE BETWEEN FLESH AND SOUL, BETWEEN LUST AND PURE LOVE.

HENCEFORTH, UNTIL HIS DYING DAY, GWENOLÉ REMAINED FREE OF LUST AND CARNAL DESIRE.

MANY YEARS LATER HE REFLECTED THAT HIS LICENTIOUS NIGHTMARE HAD BEEN THE LAST HE EVER EXPERIENCED.

DAHUD DID COME AGAIN TO HIM IN A DREAM, TO GUIDE HIM ALONG THE PATH OF JUSTICE AND TOLERANCE.

WITH GILDAS' MONASTERY BEHIND HIM, HIS THOUGHTS TURNED TO GWYNLAN, WHOSE RETURN HE WAS SO ANXIOUS TO SEE. LITTLE DID HE KNOW THE DRUID WAS SO FAR AWAY FROM THE SHORES OF BRITTANY.

AAAAAAAARGH!

HUMPH!

CRAC

HE STILL LIVES!

BRING HIM BACK UP!

AAAGH!

THE PICTS ARE NEARLY AS HARDY AS OUR MEN! WE'LL HAVE SOME FUN WITH THEM.

WHEN YOUR TURN COMES, BROTHER BRENDAN, DO YOU THINK YOUR GOD WILL LIFT YOU ON THE WINGS OF DOVES?

HE IS NOT A GOD OF THIS WORLD, OLAF! HIS KINGDOM IS IN HEAVEN!

PITY... TOO FAR AWAY TO HELP YOU, THEN!

HA! HA! HA! HA!

HURL HIM AGAIN!

THE NORTHMEN'S CHIEFTAIN BAYED FOR BLOOD.

ONCE AGAIN, THE PICT WAS THROWN OVER THE CLIFF EDGE, AND THEN ONCE MORE BEFORE HE FINALLY PERISHED.

MEANWHILE, THE FOLLOWERS OF ESUS TURNED THEIR ATTENTION TO THE STONE OF DESTINY, A STONE DESIRED BY SO MANY.

I TRUST I WILL HAVE NO REASON TO REGRET VENTURING HERE WITH ONE VERSED IN THE DRUIDS' LORE. WHAT DOES THE STONE SAY?

MASTER, WITH ALL THAT HAS PASSED IN BRITTANY, YOU SHOULD HAVE CALLED ON ME SOONER.

DO NOT BE INSOLENT.

WHAT ELSE CAN BEFALL ME? MY DEATH BY YOUR HAND? I KNOW I AM A BURDEN TO YOU, BUT I AM ALSO NECESSARY TO YOUR CAUSE.

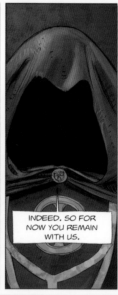

INDEED. SO FOR NOW YOU REMAIN WITH US.

VERY WELL. I CAN NOW REVEAL THAT YOU NEED NOT KEEP GWYNLAN ALIVE ANY LONGER.

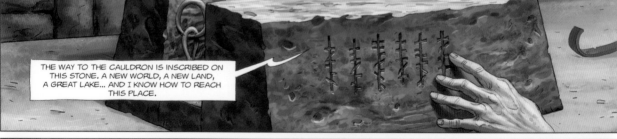

THE WAY TO THE CAULDRON IS INSCRIBED ON THIS STONE. A NEW WORLD, A NEW LAND, A GREAT LAKE... AND I KNOW HOW TO REACH THIS PLACE.

LET THE NORTHMEN KILL GWYNLAN. WE NO LONGER NEED HIM.

WHERE IS GWYNLAN?

WHY HAS HE LEFT US WITHOUT HIS WISE WORDS OF ADVICE IN THIS, OUR HOUR OF NEED?

HE'S NOT LEFT US. HE'S ATTEMPTING TO PROVE OUR INNOCENCE.

OUR INNOCENCE?

YES... SEVERAL MONKS HAVE BEEN KILLED. THOSE RESPONSIBLE LEFT BEHIND THEM OGHAM MESSAGES.

INSCRIPTIONS DESIGNED TO INCRIMINATE...

...TO INCRIMINATE...

...US!

47

BACK IN OUR OWN LAND, ROME AND ITS ALLIES FELL AS HAWKS ON THE LAST OF THE DRUIDS.

BUT FAR AWAY FROM HOME, MY MASTER, GWYNLAN, AND I, TARAN, HAD REACHED THE ISLE OF AILBE TO ASSIST A CLAN OF PICTS RECOVER THEIR STONE OF DESTINY, STOLEN FROM THEM BY A BAND OF MARAUDING NORTHMEN.

THIS STONE WAS A PATH TO OUR OWN OBJECTIVE, THE CAULDRON OF REBIRTH, ALSO COVETED BY THOSE WITH THE MONKS' BLOOD ON THEIR HANDS, THE SHADOWY DISCIPLES OF ESUS.

WHAT WOULD THE STONE REVEAL?

SOON, WE WOULD KNOW...

ON OUR HEELS, TWELVE ARMED NORTHMEN, THEIR SOLE MALEVOLENT INTENTION TO DESPATCH OUR PICTISH FRIENDS.

TWELVE STRONG, PROUD NORTHMEN, THEIR MUSCLED LIMBS GLEAMING.

THEIR EYES REVEALED ASSURED CONFIDENCE, THEIR BELIEF THAT THEY WOULD TAKE THEIR ADVERSARIES BY SURPRISE...

...WHICH SOON FADED WITH A TUMULT FROM ABOVE...

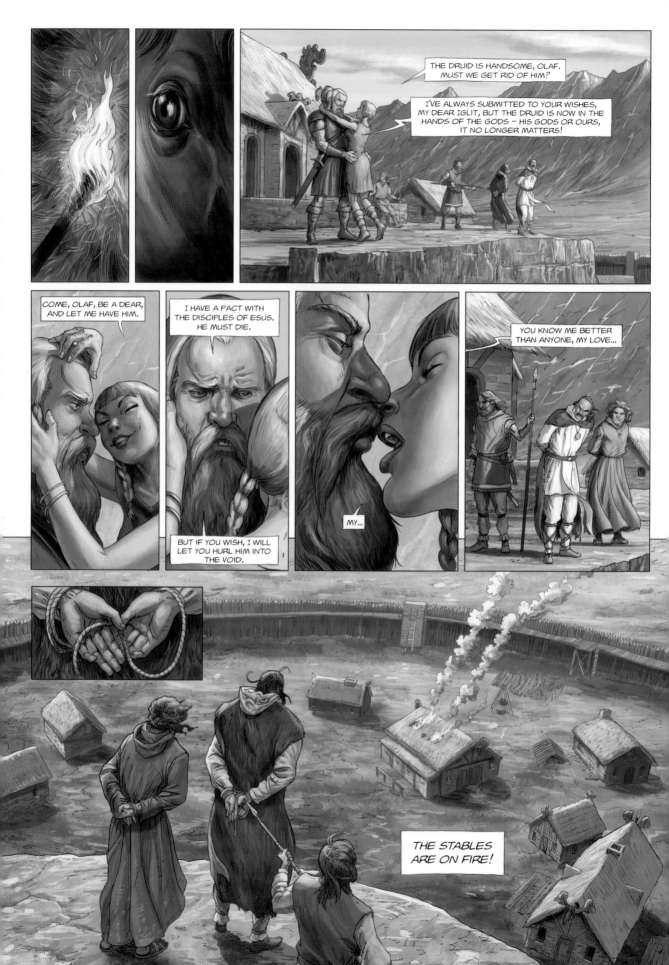

ONE OF THEM MUST BE AT LARGE.

FIND HIM!

FIND HIM AND BRING HIM TO ME!

YOU WILL SOON DIE, SWEET DRUID.

YOU ARE MAD.

IS IT WISE OF YOU TO MOCK ME, WHEN I HOLD YOUR LIFE IN MY HANDS?

I HAVE NO FEAR OF DEATH.

BUT YOUR DEATH WILL NOT COME QUICKLY. YOU WILL SUFFER! HOW MANY TIMES WILL YOU NEED TO FALL BEFORE YOU DEPART, MY GORGEOUS DRUID?

GO ON... TRY AND GUESS!

WHAT ABOUT YOURSELF? HOW NEAR IS YOUR OWN END?

WHAT?

LOOK!

DAMN THEM!

KILL THAT DRUID, AT ONCE!

I AM BUT A FAITHFUL WIFE OBEYING HER HUSBAND'S ORDERS, PRETTY DRUID.

AND HE ORDERS ME TO KILL YOU!

INDEED HE DOES.

?

NOOOOOO!

OBEY HIM IF YOU WISH!

AND DRINK TO MY HEALTH WITH YOUR GODS!

FORGIVE ME FOR THAT, BRENDAN!

I DO HOPE THIS CARNAGE CAN BE JUSTIFIED...

I AM IN TURMOIL, GWYNLAN. HAS GOD ABANDONED ME?

I CANNOT GUIDE YOU ALONG YOUR PATH, BUT I KNOW THOSE MEN IN BLACK ROBES ARE AS MUCH THE ENEMIES OF YOUR GOD AS THEY ARE OF MINE.

I FEAR THOSE DARK SOULS HAVE ALREADY LEFT THIS ISLAND.

YES... THEY NO LONGER NEED ME TO LEAD THEM TO THE CAULDRON. THEY KNOW ITS LOCATION, AND HOW TO GET THERE.

EMBROILED IN SUCH A VIOLENT ENCOUNTER, MEN METED OUT DEATH WITH EASE.

RAAAAAAGH!

IT SEEMED AS IF BRIDEI WAS CARRIED BY THE GOD OF WAR.

OUR ALLIES, THOUGH, SOON OVERCAME THE NORTHMEN.

IN PREVIOUS TIMES, NORTHMEN HAD MASSACRED PICTS TO SNATCH THE STONE OF DESTINY.

NOW, THOSE VICTIMS HAD GAINED REVENGE AND RETRIEVED WHAT WAS RIGHTLY THEIRS.

KLING

AN UNREAL FRENZY ENRAGED EACH AND EVERY COMBATTANT.

THAT DAY, BLOODY JUSTICE WAS DISCHARGED.

TALORGAN WAS RIGHT WHEN HE TOLD US THAT, IN EXCHANGE FOR OUR ASSISTANCE, WE WOULD LEARN HOW TO FIND THE CAULDRON.

ALL IS WRITTEN IN THE STONE.

IT GIVES DIRECTIONS TO THE CAULDRON, AND DESCRIBES EXACTLY WHERE TO FIND IT.

SO FAR AWAY...

YOU CAN READ OGHAM?

YES, I CAN. THE STONE POINTS US TOWARDS A LAND TO THE WEST, THE SAME PLACE THAT I MENTIONED THE NIGHT WE FIRST MET.

THE DISTANCE DID WORRY ME. TIR NA N'OG IS NORMALLY BEYOND OUR REACH. BUT IT'S A REFUGE FOR THE CAULDRON, FAR FROM THE EYES OF THOSE WHO COVET IT!

TO GET THERE WE WILL HAVE TO ENDURE AN UNBEARABLE, FROZEN LAND.

WE MUST PREPARE FOR THE WORST. WILL YOU COME WITH US, BROTHER BRENDAN?

TO MY MASTER IT WAS EVIDENT THAT BRENDAN HAD ALREADY BEEN TO THESE DISTANT LANDS.

BRENDAN HAD STUDIED REPORTS BY PHOENICIAN SAILORS AND THE ACCOUNTS OF PYTHEAS. HE KNEW ALL THE LEGENDS OF AMAZING VOYAGES AS TOLD BY THE BRITONS AND GAELS. HIS ASSISTANCE WOULD BE INVALUABLE.

BRENDAN AGREED. IT WAS A JOURNEY HE WISHED TO WITNESS.

AS WE LEFT AILBE AND HEADED WHERE NO CHRISTIAN HAD VENTURED BEFORE, I SENSED A TOUCH OF SINFUL PRIDE IN BRENDAN – ALTHOUGH HE HAD ALWAYS SEARCHED FOR GOD'S HAND IN CREATION BY FOLLOWING HIS DESTINY, RELYING ON HIMSELF AND HIS GOOD JUDGEMENT.

AS HE RELIED ON HIS GOD, OTHERS RELIED ON AN UNKNOWN MASTER.

OUR COURSE FOLLOWED A COASTLINE OF DAZZLING WHITE BEAUTY. THE BITING COLD CHILLED US THROUGH OUR THICK FURS, OUR EXPOSED SKIN FROZEN – BUT NOTHING COULD DIMINISH OUR FASCINATION WITH THIS MAGNIFICENT LANDSCAPE.

HERE, THE BEAR – OUR MOST DEIFIED CREATURE – PRESENTED AN EVEN MORE MAGNIFICENT VISION OF STRENGTH AND STATURE.

ITS PELT OF UNBLEMISHED WHITE.

AT HOME IN THE SNOW...

OUR BOAT WAS EQUIPPED FOR THIS JOURNEY. BRENDAN HAD WARNED US THAT THE GREATEST DANGER WOULD BE THE BITING COLD AND GNAWING HUNGER. A COVER OF SKINS HAD BEEN ADDED TO KEEP THE WIND AT BAY, A STOCK OF MUTTON AND DRIED FISH STOWED ABOARD, AS WELL AS PLENTY OF FRESH WATER AND ALE.

AS WE CURSED THE CHILLING WIND, WE WERE ALSO GLAD OF ITS PRESENCE, CARRYING US EVEN CLOSER TO OUR DESTINATION.

ON THE TENTH DAY, BROTHER ILLTUD BEGAN TO WITHER.

I HAD BROUGHT MY CURES AND POTIONS WITH ME ON THIS JOURNEY, BUT DESPITE THE CARE I TENDED ON BROTHER ILLTUD, A FEVER WEAKENED HIM DANGEROUSLY.

ONE EVENING, HIS STATE VERGING ON DELIRIOUS, HE CONFESSED TO US HIS SINS.

GWYNLAN ATTEMPTED TO GLEAN THE IDENTITY OF OUR OPPONENTS FROM ILLTUD – BUT IN VAIN, THE DYING MONK HAD NEVER SEEN THEIR FACES.

EMACIATED, ILLTUD HAD SUCCUMBED TO THIS VOYAGE. HIS VOICE WEAK, HE BEGGED US TO RETURN HIM TO HIS MONASTERY IN BRITTANY.

IT WAS HE WHO HAD PASSED INFORMATION TO THE DISCIPLES OF ESUS. HIS DISCLOSURES HAD LED THEM TO AILBE.

HIS VOICE NOW WEAK AND BREATH SO FOUL, THESE WERE HIS FINAL REVELATIONS. THE FEVER TOOK HIM, FREEING BROTHER ILLTUD FROM HIS EXISTENCE OF RESENTMENT, FEAR, AND PITIFUL STUPIDITY.

DEUS DEMITTIT.

EGO AUTEM NON DIMITTO.

TWO MORE BROTHERS SUCCUMBED – MAWDEZ ALSO WEAKENED, BUT CLUNG ON TO HIS SOUL.

OUR SUPPLIES WERE ALMOST GONE.

OF US ALL, I WAS THE STRONGEST.

AS THE BEAR APPROACHED, SO MANY QUESTIONS RACED THROUGH MY MIND. HAD IT BEEN FOLLOWING US OVER THE PAST DAYS? COULD IT SMELL DEATH AMONG US?

OR WAS IT THE HARBINGER OF OUR DEMISE?

IN VICTORY, THE BEAR DID SOMETHING UNEXPECTED.

IT FLED.

COME BACK!

I CHASED THE NIMBLE CREATURE, WITH NO CHANCE OF CATCHING IT...

THEN, MIRACULOUSLY...

I APPROACHED SLOWLY, HESITANT LEST IT FLED AGAIN.

BUT IT STOPPED, TO LOOK AT ME.

I'M SORRY, BUT WE NEED TO EAT YOUR MEAT...

ROOA AAAR

IT LEFT ME, ALONE ON THE ICE. I WAS READY TO RELINQUISH MY SOUL.

THEN...

...I SAW SOME SEALS, NOT LONG KILLED BY THE BEAR.

SALVATION FROM ABOVE.

AS WE TRAVAILED, GWENOLÉ, RECLUSIVE IN HIS MONASTERY AT LANDEVENEG, WAS DEEP IN THOUGHT...

...ASHAMED HOW VERUS TREATED THE LAST OF THE DRUIDS. ASHAMED OF BELONGING TO A CHURCH WHOSE FOUNDER PREACHED LOVE AND COMPASSION – BUT WHOSE LATTER DAY SERVANTS BAYED FOR THE BLOOD OF THOSE WHO DID NOT FOLLOW THEIR CREED.

GWENOLÉ RECOGNISED HIS ROLE IN THIS CALUMNY. BUT HE HAD NOW CHANGED. MORALLY, HE WAS UNABLE TO PERMIT THE CHURCH WANTONLY TO DESTROY THE REMNANTS OF THE DRUIDIC ORDER.

AS A SLEEPLESS NIGHT CLOSED IN, HE DID WHAT CAME FIRST TO CHRISTIANS.

HE PRAYED FOR GUIDANCE.

SUBMITTING TO THE LORD.

WITHOUT HOPE...

...UNTIL SUNRISE, WITH NEW LIGHT BATHING THE GREY EARTH. THEN GWENOLÉ SMILED.

THE LIGHT SHOWED THE WAY...

...A WAY TO SAVE THE FEW REMAINING DRUIDS.

HE COULD SAVE THEM.

OUR PROGRESS WAS SLOW THROUGH THIS SAVAGE COUNTRY...

...THROUGH FORESTS MUCH DENSER THAT THOSE AT HOME.

KRACK

"THEY... THEY KILLED THEM ALL."

"WE WELCOMED THEM AS GODS FROM ACROSS THE SEA, BUT THE DEMONS KILLED MY WHOLE FAMILY!"

WHAT IS SHE SAYING?

I HAVE NO IDEA!

SHE SAYS THE DEMONS ARE HERE!

SHE SAYS THEY CAME FROM OVER THE SEA. THEY WELCOMED THEM AS GODS. BUT THEY WERE DECEIVED!

THESE DEMONS ABUSED OUR WOMEN, AND KILLED OUR MEN, CHILDREN AND ELDERS.

I WOULD VENTURE THAT YOUR ADVERSARIES HAVE ARRIVED, GWYNLAN, AND LEFT THEIR MARK.

WHO ARE YOU, OLD MAN? HOW DO YOU SPEAK OUR TONGUE?

I SPEAK YOUR TONGUE AS MY FATHER DID. HE WAS ONE OF YOU BUT MY MOTHER WAS FROM THIS LAND. I SPEAK BOTH TONGUES, BUT I HAVE NOT SPOKEN YOURS FOR MANY YEARS.

DID YOUR FATHER COME HERE WITH THE CAULDRON?

CAULDRON? WHAT CAULDRON?

THE MEN WHO CAME AHEAD OF US SEEK IT AND WILL KILL FOR IT. THEY ARE OUR ENEMIES.

THE GIRL HAS A FEVER...

CAN WE TAKE HER SOMEWHERE?

FOLLOW ME!

66

SHE'LL BE FINE. SHE ISN'T BADLY HURT. SHE'S JUST TERRIFIED AND IN SHOCK. I'LL HELP HER SLEEP.

SLEEP WILL HELP HEAL HER SOUL. TIME WILL DO THE REST.

YOU ARE A WISE SHAMAN.

A SHAMAN?

THAT IS WHAT WE CALL A MAN WHO HEALS.

THAT IS WHAT HE IS. TARAN CAN HEAL YOUR FRIEND.

MY NAME IS GWYNLAN. WHAT IS YOURS, OLD MAN?

HERE, MY NAME MEANS "SON OF THE SEA". IN THE BRITISH TONGUE, YOU SAY "MORGAN".

I AM BRENDAN. WHAT ARE THE WOMAN'S PEOPLE CALLED?

THE INNU.

CAN YOU TAKE US TO HER VILLAGE?

TO THE OTHERS, THOSE SHE CALLED DEMONS?

PLEASE BELIEVE ME, MORGAN. WE ARE NOT WITH THEM.

THAT, I DO NOT KNOW. THEY MAY BE YOUR ENEMIES. OR THEY MAY NOT BE.

BROTHER MAWDEZ?

YES?

WE HAVE A PROBLEM.

68

PREACHING OUR MESSAGE OF PEACE WILL BE FUTILE!

HE'S A CHRISTIAN!

I KNOW THAT!

HE'S BATTLED AGAINST US... HE IS ONE OF OUR MAIN FOES.

TRUE. BUT HE HAS BATTLED AGAINST US WITHOUT THE FORCE OF ARMS. HIS FORCE ARE HIS WORDS, ATTEMPTING TO DEMONSTRATE THE SUPERIORITY OF HIS GOD.

AND THAT'S WHY YOU ASK US NOW TO HEAR THIS DAMNED MONK?!

I WANT US TO HEAR HIM BECAUSE HE IS SINCERE IN WHAT HE HAS TO SAY, EVEN IF WE DECIDE NOT TO ACCEPT HIS WORDS.

I ALSO KNOW THAT HIS SOLE INTENTION IS TO HELP US IN OUR SURVIVAL.

COME!

WE WILL HEAR YOU, BROTHER GWENOLÉ.

WHO ARE THESE MEN?

BRAVE HUNTERS WHO BRING ME SUSTENANCE.

INNU BRAVES, INTRIGUED BY YOUR FACES AND GARMENTS. THEY THINK YOU ARE SPIRITS.

"AMAGUK... TELL YOUR MEN THERE IS NO DANGER. THESE ARE NOT SPIRITS, BUT MEN FROM A LAND TO THE EAST OF THE GREAT ICE."

"THEY STINK!"

HA! HA! HA!

WHAT IS IT, MORGAN?

NOTHING, NOTHING!

"AMAGUK, THE MASAARAK VILLAGE WAS ATTACKED BY OTHER STRANGERS."

"NUKKA SAYS MANY OF OUR FRIENDS DIED."

"WHAT DO YOU SAY?"

"I WILL TAKE THESE MEN TO THE GREAT LAKE. I WANT YOU TO MEET US THERE WITH YOUR BRAVEST WARRIORS. ASK AKIAK TO COME WITH YOU. BUT KEEP OUT OF SIGHT UNTIL I GIVE YOU THE SIGNAL."

"VERY WELL."

"TAKE CARE, SON OF THE SEA."

WHERE ARE THEY GOING?

TO GATHER SUPPORT. AFTER WHAT NUKKA TOLD US, WE WILL NEED MORE HELP.

YOU WANTED TO MEET YOUR ENEMIES, GWYNLAN... THEN COME! I WILL TAKE YOU TO THE MASAARAK VILLAGE ON THE GREAT LAKE.

LET ME STAY. THE YOUNG GIRL CAN'T BE ALONE.

TARAN, WE'LL NEED YOU WITH US. ONE OF THE MONKS CAN CARE FOR HER.

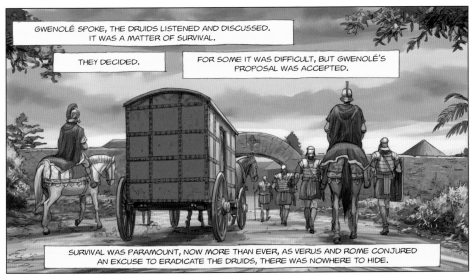

GWENOLÉ SPOKE, THE DRUIDS LISTENED AND DISCUSSED.
IT WAS A MATTER OF SURVIVAL.

THEY DECIDED.

FOR SOME IT WAS DIFFICULT, BUT GWENOLÉ'S
PROPOSAL WAS ACCEPTED.

SURVIVAL WAS PARAMOUNT, NOW MORE THAN EVER, AS VERUS AND ROME CONJURED
AN EXCUSE TO ERADICATE THE DRUIDS, THERE WAS NOWHERE TO HIDE.

THE DRUIDS HAD ALWAYS BEEN
ATTUNED TO NATURE...

AND NATURE WOULD
ADAPT AND SURVIVE...

GWENOLÉ'S PLAN HAD REACHED THE
EARS OF ARCHBISHOP VERUS WHO
PROCEEDED TO THE MONASTERY AT
LANDEVENEG TO SEE FOR HIMSELF.

BROTHER
GWENOLÉ.

IT IS A PLEASURE TO SEE
YOU AGAIN, LORD VERUS...

I COULD HAVE DONE WITHOUT
THIS VISIT HERE. I HAVE BEEN
TOLD YOU ARE CONCEALING
DRUIDS IN THE VERY HEART
OF YOUR MONASTERY...

YOU ARE MISINFORMED.
THERE ARE NO DRUIDS HERE.

I WILL SEE
FOR MYSELF!

AS YOU WISH...

WHAT I HAVE HEARD
IS TRUE.

MISINFORMED? NO!
I RECOGNISE THESE MEN...
THEY ARE DRUIDS!

PLEASE LET ME CORRECT
YOU, LORD VERUS. THEY
WERE FORMERLY DRUIDS.

FORMERLY, YOU SAY?

THEIR ALLEGIANCE IS NOW TO
THE ONE GOD AND HIS CHURCH!

THEY PLACED THEIR
SOULS AT THE MERCY
OF CHRIST.

GWENOLÉ, YOU ARE A DECEITFUL
VIPER. I UNDERESTIMATED YOU.

YOU ARE PROTECTING DRUIDS BY
DRESSING THEM UP AS MONKS!

THERE IS MORE
TO A MONK THAN
HIS HABIT!

I HAVE NO REASON TO DOUBT THEIR SINCERITY.

THINK AGAIN. THEY WILL NEVER RENOUNCE THEIR FAITH. THEY WILL PRAY TO GOD IN YOUR PRESENCE AND DEVOTE THEMSELVES TO LUGH BEHIND YOUR BACK. THEY ARE DEMONS, GWENOLÉ. AND WE MUST RID OURSELVES OF DEMONS.

YOU ARE VERY VEHEMENT IN YOUR STRUGGLE AGAINST THE DRUID ORDER.

DO YOU FORGET THAT THEY HAVE MURDERED CHRISTIANS?

IN TRUTH, IT IS NOT THEY WHO ARE GUILTY OF KILLING THOSE MONKS.

THE TRUTH IS WELL KNOWN... AND WE KNOW THAT YOU ASSOCIATE WITH THOSE WHO KILLED THE MONKS.

DO YOU DARE DOUBT ME?

YOU HAVE YOUR EYES, I HAVE MINE. ONE OF YOUR MEETINGS WITH THESE HOODED MEN DID NOT ESCAPE MY INFORMANTS.

IT IS TIME, LORD VERUS, TO CONFESS FOR THE GOOD OF YOUR SOUL.

IT WAS A BLUFF. GWENOLÉ HAD REACHED HIS CONCLUSION BY MERE DEDUCTION.

HIS EYES WERE NOWHERE CLOSE TO VERUS.

WITH CONFESSIONS AT HOME, ACROSS THE OCEAN IT WAS OUR TIME TO FIND OUR WAY TO THE TRUTH.

HERE IS THE VILLAGE!

DOES THIS LAKE LEAD TO THE SEA?

YES, BY A RIVER FURTHER WEST.

YOU SAY THEY SEEK A CAULDRON?

THE CAULDRON OF REBIRTH, BROUGHT HERE BY THE PICTS.

BUT WHY BRING A CAULDRON HERE?

TO SAVE IT FROM FALLING INTO THE WRONG HANDS... TO ENSURE THE SURVIVAL OF THE GODS' AND DRUIDS' POWER IN THE AGE OF THE NEW CHURCH. BUT YOU ALREADY KNOW THIS AS WELL AS I DO, DON'T YOU, MORGAN?

I HAD TO BE SURE OF YOUR INTENTIONS. THOSE WHO CAME FIRST DID NOT COME IN PEACE.

WHERE IS THE CAULDRON, MORGAN?

NEARBY, IN THAT CAVE BEYOND.

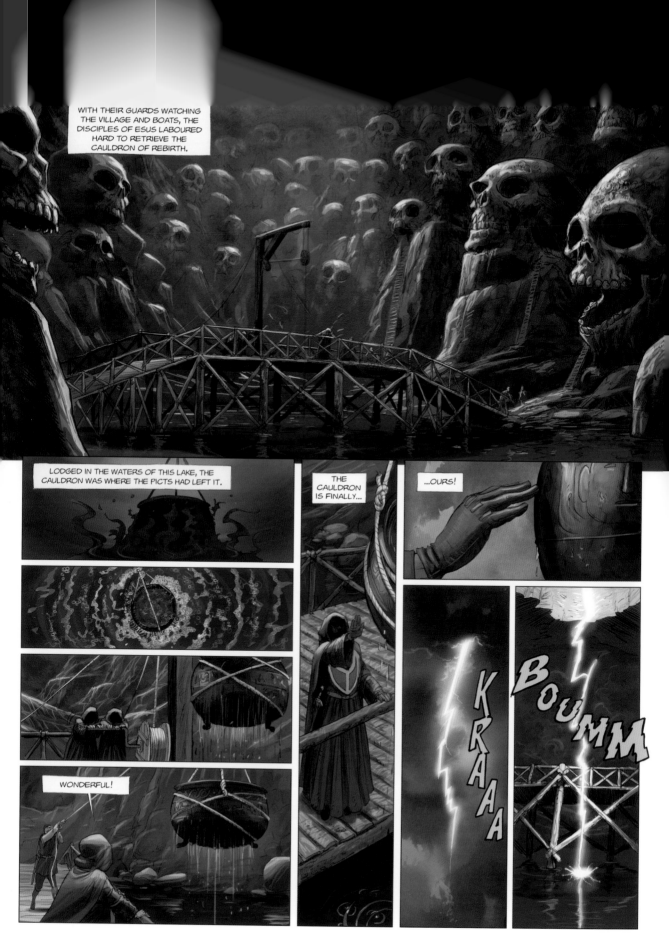

WITH THEIR GUARDS WATCHING THE VILLAGE AND BOATS, THE DISCIPLES OF ESUS LABOURED HARD TO RETRIEVE THE CAULDRON OF REBIRTH.

LODGED IN THE WATERS OF THIS LAKE, THE CAULDRON WAS WHERE THE PICTS HAD LEFT IT.

THE CAULDRON IS FINALLY...

...OURS!

WONDERFUL!

KRAAA

BOUMM

THE POWER OF THIS TALISMAN HAS AGAIN BROUGHT DOWN THE WRATH OF THE HEAVENS...

ONCE MORE, THE ELEMENTS ARE UNLEASHED!

SUCH IS THE DARK POWER OF ESUS!

SUCH IS THE RIGHTEOUS WRATH OF LUGH!

YOU?

THE CAULDRON GAVE THE INNU PROTECTION. THEY WILL HOLD YOU TO ACCOUNT...

BY ESUS, GWYNLAN! I THOUGHT I HAD SEEN THE LAST OF YOU!

THE TONE OF YOUR VOICE HAS CHANGED.

BECAUSE I NO LONGER NEED TO HIDE, MY FRIEND. YOUR JOURNEY ENDS HERE.

BUDOG...

...I HAVE KNOWN YOU ALL MY LIFE...

BROOOMMMM

I HAD STAYED OUTSIDE WITH MORGAN AND BRENDAN TO SEE HOW WE COULD FREE THE VILLAGERS TAKEN BY THE DISCIPLES OF ESUS AND THEIR MERCENARIES.

MORGAN'S MIND PLAYED WITH DARK MEMORIES OF HIS MASSACRED KIN, THEIR BLOOD POOLING ON THE SODDEN GROUND.

I COUNT TWENTY SEVEN!

DID YOU COUNT HIM?

NO...

THAT MAKES TWENTY EIGHT GUARDS AND THREE MEN IN CAPES.

AS WELL AS THOSE INSIDE THE CAVE.

DO YOU THINK NUKKA WILL BRING ENOUGH MEN?

I DON'T KNOW. BUT THEY ARE NOT EXPECTING AN ATTACK HERE. NO-ONE IS GUARDING THE VILLAGE.

TARAN! LOOK! MAWDEZ!

WHAT...?

HE'S GOING TO GWYNLAN.

76

AS OLD ACQUAINTANCES, GWYNLAN, LET'S NOT MAKE THIS TOO DIFFICULT.

I DID NOT WANT YOU TO SUSPECT ME...

I CAN SEE I MAY HAVE DISAPPOINTED YOU. I HAVE DECEIVED YOU, BUT THE TRUTH WE SEEK CAN ONLY BE REVEALED THROUGH DEVIOUSNESS AND TREACHERY.

OUR GOAL WAS WORTHY, HOWEVER ACHIEVED.

IF THE TRUTH SHOULD BE REVEALED TO ALL, IT SHOULD REQUIRE NO LIES.

UNLESS OTHER LIES OBSTRUCT THE WAY TO THE TRUTH. YOU DRUIDS HAVE ALWAYS LIED.

WE WILL NOT SEE EYE TO EYE, GWYNLAN. ANY ATTEMPT TO CONVERT YOU WOULD HAVE BEEN FUTILE BECAUSE OF YOUR RIGHTEOUS VIEW OF THE WORLD, CONSTRUCTED TO AVOID ACCEPTING TRUTH.

YOU THEN SUGGESTED MY NAME TO GWENOLÉ SO YOU COULD KEEP A CHECK ON ME.

YES, TO KEEP YOU FROM OBSTRUCTING OUR WORK.

YOUR WORK WAS ALREADY UNDERWAY. YOU PLANNED EVERYTHING OUT, DIDN'T YOU?

CORRECT, GWENOLÉ! I DO CONFESS THAT I PUT EVERYTHING IN PLACE TO FINISH OFF THE DRUIDS.

IT WAS SO EASY. THE DRUIDS REJECT THE WRITTEN WORD... THEY ARE THEREFORE MUTE. ONCE GONE, WHO WILL REMEMBER THEM?

IN BRITAIN WE FORGED AN ORDER TO DEFEND THE CHRISTIAN FAITH – THE HOLY VENGEANCE.

ITS LEADING LIGHT, PADRIG.

WE – VERUS, MYSELF AND OTHERS – TASKED THE ORDER TO BRING THE NEAR-HERETICAL BRITISH CHURCH TO HEEL.

A LAUDABLE GOAL TO RETAIN ROME'S SUPREMACY.

WE TOILED FOR THE UNITY OF THE HOLY ROMAN CHURCH. THERE WOULD BE NO SALVATION FOR ANYONE OUTSIDE HER.

THE HOLY VENGEANCE WAS DISBANDED BY CONSTANTINE BEFORE WE REACHED OUR GOAL. WITH CHRISTIANITY DECREED LAWFUL BY THE NEW EMPEROR, DID OUR CONTINUED EXISTENCE REMAIN NECESSARY?

ONLY LATER, IN BRITTANY, DID VERUS DECIDE TO REUNITE THE FEW REMAINING MEMBERS OF OUR SECRET ORDER.

OUR OBJECTIVE WAS TO CONCLUDE OUR STALLED MISSION...

...AND FINISH OFF THE DRUIDS!

EVEN YOU, GWENOLÉ, WILL AGREE THAT NONE BUT OUR HEAVENLY FATHER MAY REIGN IN BRITTANY.

THE LORD ALREADY REIGNS HERE. WOULD HE WISH THE DRUIDS DEAD? OBSERVANCE OF HIS DOMAIN WOULD SUFFICE. HIS FIRST COMMANDMENT TELLS US NOT TO KILL.

YOU ARE AN IDEALIST IN A FAR FROM IDEAL WORLD.

AN IDEALIST IN A LIVING NIGHTMARE.

TO GET RID OF THE DRUIDS YOU ACCUSED THEM OF KILLING THOSE MONKS – AN EXCUSE TO IMPRISON AND EXECUTE MY BROTHERS. WITHOUT SUCH AN EXCUSE, THE DRUIDS WOULD HAVE BEEN MARTYRS TO PROGRESS.

A VERY REGRETTABLE COINCIDENCE... OUR MAIN OBJECTIVE WAS TO ERADICATE YOUR MEMORY.

WITHOUT HISTORY, WITHOUT MEMORY, YOU WOULD NEVER HAVE EXISTED.

THOSE TRANSLATORS HAD TO DIE, TAKING WITH THEM THE SECRETS OF THEIR MANUSCRIPTS...

BUT, AS GOD IS MY WITNESS, THAT WAS NOT OUR ORIGINAL COURSE.

THE FIRST MONK'S DEATH WAS UNPLANNED. HE WANTED TO SHARE THE SECRETS OF THOSE SCROLLS WITH OTHER SCHOLARS HE KNEW. WE TOLD HIM TO KEEP HIS COUNSEL, BUT HIS TONGUE WAS LOOSE.

GURVAN WAS ENRAGED AND FELL UPON HIM WITH HIS OWN HANDS.

LORD HAVE MERCY. IT WAS A TERRIBLE ACCIDENT.

IT WAS A BAD FALL, NOTHING MORE. THE TRANSLATOR DIED INSTANTLY.

IT WAS VERUS WHO DECIDED TO BLAME THE DRUIDS.

HIS PLAN WAS PERFECT. AS A DANGER TO ALL INNOCENT FOLK, NO-ONE WOULD MOURN YOUR PASSING.

WE KNEW JUST ABOUT ENOUGH TO USE YOUR SYMBOLS AGAINST YOU.

BUT LET THE PAST GO.

THE CAULDRON OF REBIRTH AND THE SPEAR OF LUGH ARE NO LONGER YOURS.

THEY NOW BELONG TO THE LORD. HENCEFORTH, THE SPEAR OF LUGH WILL BE THE LANCE OF LONGINIUS WHICH PIERCED THE SIDE OF OUR SAVIOUR, THE CAULDRON WILL BECOME THE HOLY GRAIL, CHRIST'S VESSEL OF ETERNAL LIFE.

ABSURD.

WHY FABRICATE SUCH A STORY ABOUT THE HOLY GRAIL?

IT WILL RING TRUE. THE GRAIL WAS BROUGHT TO BRITAIN BY JOSEPH OF ARIMATHEA, AND STOLEN BY THE PICTS – THAT IS, THE CAULDRON OF REBIRTH. I POSSES A MANUSCRIPT BEARING WITNESS TO THIS.

AND THE LANCE? IT WAS PASSED AROUND UNTIL IT FINALLY REACHED THE HANDS OF A DRUID. SUCH A STRANGE COINCIDENCE.

LOOK ME IN MY EYE, GWYNLAN, AND TELL ME WHO LIES AND WHO HAS THE TRUTH?

YOU OR ME?

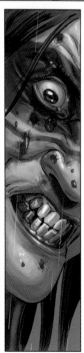

WHY ESUS?
WHY CHOOSE A GOD
OF THE CELTS?

ESUS IS A REFERENCE TO YOUR DEMISE,
GWYNLAN. SIMPLY A SYMBOL. HIS NAME
REFLECTS THAT OF JESUS.

IT MEANS THE OLD FAITH
WILL GIVE WAY TO THE NEW.

WE REJECT THESE ANCIENT GODS. WE KNOW
THERE ONLY EXISTS THE ONE AND ONLY ALMIGHTY
AND HIS SON THE MESSIAH, THE CHRIST.

BUT WE'VE
TALKED
ENOUGH.

WE NEED TO MAKE OUR
WAY BACK TO ROME
WITH THE CAULDRON –
OR RATHER, THE GRAIL.

TELL ME,
GWYNLAN, WHAT
BECAME OF
YOUR TRAVELLING
COMPANIONS?

I AM HERE,
BUDOG.

MAWDEZ!

STAY WHERE YOU
ARE, MAWDEZ!

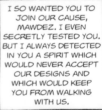

I HEARD WHAT YOU SAID
AND I UNDERSTAND
WHAT YOU MEAN, AND
BELIEVE AS YOU DO
IN GOD, BUT I COULD
NEVER MAKE SUCH A
SACRIFICE.

I SO WANTED YOU TO
JOIN OUR CAUSE,
MAWDEZ. I EVEN
SECRETLY TESTED YOU.
BUT I ALWAYS DETECTED
IN YOU A SPIRIT WHICH
WOULD NEVER ACCEPT
OUR DESIGNS AND
WHICH WOULD KEEP
YOU FROM WALKING
WITH US.

RETURN TO US...
OUR LORD DOES
NOT PREACH HATE
OR VENGEANCE.
HE IS THE GOD OF
FORGIVENESS.

MAWDEZ, YOUR
WORDS MOVE ME!
YOU BELIEVE I COULD
RETURN TO YOUR PATH.
BUT IT IS YOU WHO
HAS GONE ASTRAY,
MY... BROTHER...

MAWDEZ, NO!
DON'T LET GO!

YOU DIDN'T
HAVE TO KILL HIM!

OF COURSE I HAD TO.

I HAD TO KILL HIM FOR
THE SAME REASON I HAD
TO KILL THE OTHER MONKS.
NO WITNESSES. ALL EVIDENCE
MUST BE DESTROYED.

WE ARE ALSO READY TO
KILL OURSELVES ONCE
OUR TASK IS DONE.

THERE IS ONLY ONE PATH IN THIS WORLD,
THE PATH TO POWER. JESUS HAS GIVEN US POWER,
AND WE WILL BE TRIUMPHANT!

I HARBOUR NO ILL FEELINGS
TOWARDS YOU, GWYNLAN.

THERE WILL BE
NO MORE STRIFE.
ETERNAL PEACE
WILL REIGN OVER
THE WORLD!

I DO THIS FOR THOSE WHO
WILL FOLLOW US, SO THAT THE
WORLD WILL LIVE UNDER
THE LOVE OF GOD.

YOU LOSE THE OLD FAITH IN THE NAME OF POWER AND PEACE, BUT YOU ARE MISGUIDED. WE ARE THE ROOTS WHICH HOLD THE EARTH TOGETHER. WITHOUT US, YOU WILL DESTROY THIS EARTH AND BE BLIND TO YOUR ACTIONS.

DON'T MAKE SUCH GROUNDLESS PREDICTIONS!

BUDOG!

WE MUST LEAVE NOW!

EVEN MORE LIES! YOU WON'T KILL YOURSELF, AND YOUR GOD WON'T GIVE ANY CREDENCE TO YOUR STUDIED WORDS. YOU MUST HAVE HAD A MORE PERSONAL REASON THAN THAT TO MURDER MAWDEZ.

YOU WERE ALWAYS ASTUTE, GWYNLAN.

VERY WELL, LET ME BE HONEST WITH YOU. WE HAVE NEARLY REACHED OUR OBJECTIVE. I AM OLD...

...OLD ON THE OUTSIDE, BUT FULL OF YOUTHFUL VIGOUR INSIDE. SOON, DEATH WILL TAKE ME AND I WILL HAVE COMPLETED ONLY SOME OF MY AIMS. THAT, YOU WILL UNDERSTAND... OR PERHAPS IT IS OF NO CONSEQUENCE...

...BUT...

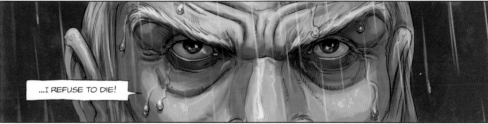

...I REFUSE TO DIE!

THIS CAULDRON WILL MAKE ME IMMORTAL AND GIVE ME THE FRUITS OF KNOWLEDGE.

LIFE AND KNOWLEDGE.

YOU WILL DIE TODAY.

HOW?

85

CRACK

YOU SHOULD KNOW THE DRUIDS BETTER. THE FOREST PROTECTS US, AND ALSO TEACHES US.

A BURROW SHOULD ALWAYS HAVE TWO WAYS OUT. YOU IMPEDED THE FIRST, BUT NOT THE SECOND, AND WE ESCAPED.

WILL YOU...

...KILL ME?

HAVE MERCY!

THE FOREST MUST HAVE YOUR BLOOD, VERUS!

MONTHS PASSED BEFORE WE REACHED OUR OWN LAND, FORESTS AND SPRINGS AGAIN. BRENDAN AND HIS COMPANIONS STAYED BEHIND TO LEARN THE CUSTOMS OF THE WONDERFUL NEW WORLD.

I WONDERED WHAT INTEREST HIS CHURCH WOULD SHOW IN THESE NATIVES LIVING IN IGNORANT SIN...

GWENOLÉ JOINED US ONCE WE REACHED THE MONASTERY ON ENEZ VRIAD.

OUR ABSENCE HAD WITNESSED MANY HORRIFIC EVENTS – SO MANY LIVES LOST, SO MANY FELLOW DRUIDS SACRIFICED ON THE ALTAR OF PERFIDIOUSNESS.

GWENOLÉ'S DEMURE WAS COMPLETELY CHANGED, SEEMING FINALLY TO HAVE FOUND PEACE.

BUT THE DRUIDS' PLACE IN TIME WAS DRAWING TO A CLOSE, FACED WITH THE PROGRESS OF THE CHRISTIAN CHURCH.

MY DAYS OF ACCOMPANYING MY MASTER WOULD EVENTUALLY END. THREATENED WITH CERTAIN DEATH OR CONTINUED SURVIVAL, I CHOSE TO FOLLOW THOSE WHO HAD ONCE BEEN OUR PERSECUTORS.

BUT, FROM WITHIN THEIR HOLY WALLS, I CAN COMMIT MY MEMORIES TO PARCHMENT, MEMORIES WHICH WILL KEEP THE DRUIDS ALIVE... MEMORIES OF MY MASTER, GWYNLAN.

people & places

AILBE
A legendary island far to the north, in the region of Iceland, famously visited by the Irish monk Brendan.

BRENDAN
The Irish abbot and saint whose legendary sea voyages are chronicled in the *Navigatio Sancti Brendani Abbatis*. He reputedly reached the 'terra repromissionis', or the distant paradise across the western ocean – could this be North America, and indeed the fabled land of youth, Tir Na n'Og of Irish legend? Ogham inscriptions were said to have been discovered on America's eastern seaboard, and experimental archaeology in the 1970s demonstrated that mariners such as Brendan could have crossed the Atlantic to North America.

BUDOG & MAWDEZ
Two monks originally from Wales who established monastic foundations in Brittany and Cornwall.

the CAULDRON OF REBIRTH
In Welsh mythology, the Cauldron of Rebirth can revive the dead to life. It plays a major role in the second branch of the *Mabinogion* legends, and has parallels with many other cauldrons in Celtic mythology. Probably the most well-known Celtic cauldron to survive is the Gundestrup Cauldron, discovered in Denmark in 1891.

CORNWALL
The south-westernmost region of Britain, it is an area that retains today a strong Celtic cultural identity and has witnessed a resurgence in the Cornish language. The language is closely related to Breton and Welsh.

DOMNONEA
The part of northern Brittany facing south-western Britain. The name is cognate with that of the kingdom of Dumnonia (comprising Devon and Cornwall) in Britain, deriving from the same Brythonic root *dumno and *nanto, meaning 'deep valley'.

ENEZ VRIAD
The Breton name for the small archipelago of Bréhat in the vicinity of Pempoull. Several monasteries were founded here by the early saints from Wales.

ESUS
This ancient Celtic god demanded human sacrifice of his followers. Victims would be stabbed, hanged in the trees and left to bleed to death. Esus is also associated with agriculture, war and commerce, and was, at one time considered cognate with Jesus because of the relevant element of the name.

the GRAIL
The mystical chalice, associated with Christ's Last Supper, of Arthurian legend. It is the inheritor of the Celtic tradition of magical cauldrons of plenty and of resurrection.

GWENOLÉ
Gwenolé was one of the first native Breton saints, disciple of Budog. According to his *Life*, Gwenolé was acquainted with some of the remaining druids of the time. His main monastery was the Abbey at Landeveneg in western Brittany, with churches dedicated to him in Wales and Cornwall, as well as in Brittany.

INNU
The indigenous inhabitants of a part of Quebec and Labrador in Canada, they were formerly known as the Algonquins. Not to be confused with the Inuit, their name in their language means "men".

LUGH
One of the main gods of the Celtic pantheon. He was considered extremely dexterous and skilful The name derives from the Celtic root for 'light'. Tradition associates Lugh with a magical spear.

MÔN
The isle of Anglesey in north Wales, called Mona by the Romans, was the druids' holy sanctuary. The island was defiled by the legions of Rome in AD 60 and AD 78.

MORRIGAN
The Celtic triple goddess who could shapeshift at will and often appeared as a crow. Her name means 'great queen'.

NA N'OG

The legendary land of eternal youth in Irish and Welsh tradition. Mortals could cross to this Otherworld and remain youthful for ever, but if they returned to the world of men and set foot on the ground they would immediately age and die.

NORTHMEN

Also known as the Vikings, these were feared seafarers from Scandinavia who left their mark on vast tracts of Europe and established kingdoms in Britain and Ireland – even sailing in their longboats as far as North America.

OGHAM

A form of writing amongst the Celts, with surviving stone inscriptions in Ireland and western Britain, especially in Wales. Each letter of the alphabet is represented by a number of strokes along a vertical axis, starting at the bottom left.

PADRIG

The Welsh spelling of Patrick, the saint who, according to his *Life*, was born in Britain in a place called Bannaventa. In AD 406, at 16 years old, he was captured by Irish raiders and taken to Ireland where he was enslaved for six years. He eventually managed to escape, return home, and was then ordained into the Church. According to one tradition, he was sent by the Pope to Britain to counter the Pelagian heresy.

PHOENICIANS

The Phoenicians were famous for their seafaring and mercantile abilities. Originating from cities such as Tyre in Lebanon, with colonies across the Mediterranean, the Phoenicians sailed to Britain to trade in tin from Cornwall.

PICTS

This generic name given to the non-Romanised tribes living beyond the Roman Empire's northern frontier in Britain marked by Hadrian's Wall. Little factual information is known about the Picts. They were considered fierce by their southern neighbours and reputedly painted their bodies in intricate patterns – the name 'Pict' means 'painted people'. Although several theories have abounded regarding their ethnicity, the Picts were most probably linguistically and culturally related to the Britons.

PYTHEAS

Pytheas was a Greek explorer from the city of Massalia – modern day Marseille. He ventured on a voyage to northern Europe around 325 BC and was the first to record sighting of the Midnight Sun and the Arctic ice fields.

SPEAR OF LONGINIUS

Traditionally, Longinius was the Roman centurion who struck his spear in the side of Christ at the Crucifixion. The spear in this story is associated with the fiery Spear of Lugh of Irish mythology.

STONE OF DESTINY

The Stone of Destiny plays a major role in Scotland's history. Also known as the Stone of Scone, it has for centuries been embroiled in controversy after being taken from Scone Abbey to London in England. Some legends refer to the stone as being the coronation stone of the Gaels of Dál Riata in western Scotland, whose kingdom was established by Irish invaders from the 6th century onwards.

VERUS

The archbishop of Tours between AD 489 and 500, whose archbishopric included Brittany. On behalf of Pope Anastasius II (AD 496-498), Verus liaised with the Celtic Church in Brittany in an attempt to reconcile the traditions of the Brythonic church and the Church of Rome.

VOYAGE OF BRÂN

A legendary Irish tale of Bran mac Febail embarking on a quest to the Otherworld. Similar in substance to the legend of Na n'Og, when Brân returns to Ireland one of his companions sets foot on the ground and turns to dust. After relating his story of life in paradise, Brân sets sail across the ocean, never to be seen again.

TAKING DRUIDS
TO AMERICA

In this final part of the *Druids* story, we've sent Gwynlan and his companions to new shores across the Atlantic. But can this be a serious proposition? Several researchers argue that the people we now call Celts – a term popularised by the 17th century Welsh linguist Edward Lhuyd – could have set foot in the New World five centuries before the Vikings. Evidence for this is scarce, even more so in the archaeological field, but the Celtic legends of Ireland and Britain point to some sense of an other world across the ocean.

The Irish imrama, or tales of voyages, suggest that Celtic seafarers knew long ago of stepping stones across the Atlantic – from Ireland, to Orkney, Iceland, Greenland and thence on to Newfoundland. There is evidence to suggest that monks from Ireland may have occupied Iceland before the Vikings reached the island, and current research by linguists in the United States suggests lexical proximity between the language of the Algonquin Indians and of Celtic languages.

The Welsh tales of Prince Madog establishing a colony in Alabama still resonate, and stories of native tribes speaking Welsh were once widespread. On sailing along the St Lawrence river in Canada, 16th century Breton explorer Jacques Cartier observed strange villages populated by people with European features. Indeed, Native American histories throw some light on this, and suggest that the Celts had arrived in the New World long before the Vikings.

In this story, we meet the 6th century monk Brendan, abbot of Clonfert. The *Navigatio* of St Brendan, containing the stories of his voyages, was in its day what we would now call a bestseller. The tales of his voyages inspired generations of Europeans to search for the 'Fortunate Isles' somewhere to the west. Could his 'Islands of Sheep' be the Faroes? Could his 'pillars of crystals' be references to icebergs? To try and answer these and other questions, explorer Tim Severin ventured to prove that Brendan could indeed have crossed the Atlantic in an Irish curragh. In 1976 he built an authentic replica of a curragh of Brendan's time and managed to sail the 4,500 miles from Ireland, via the Hebrides and Iceland to Newfoundland and back.

Evidence, perhaps not, but enough to allow us to imagine this fictional possibility.

Thierry Jigourel

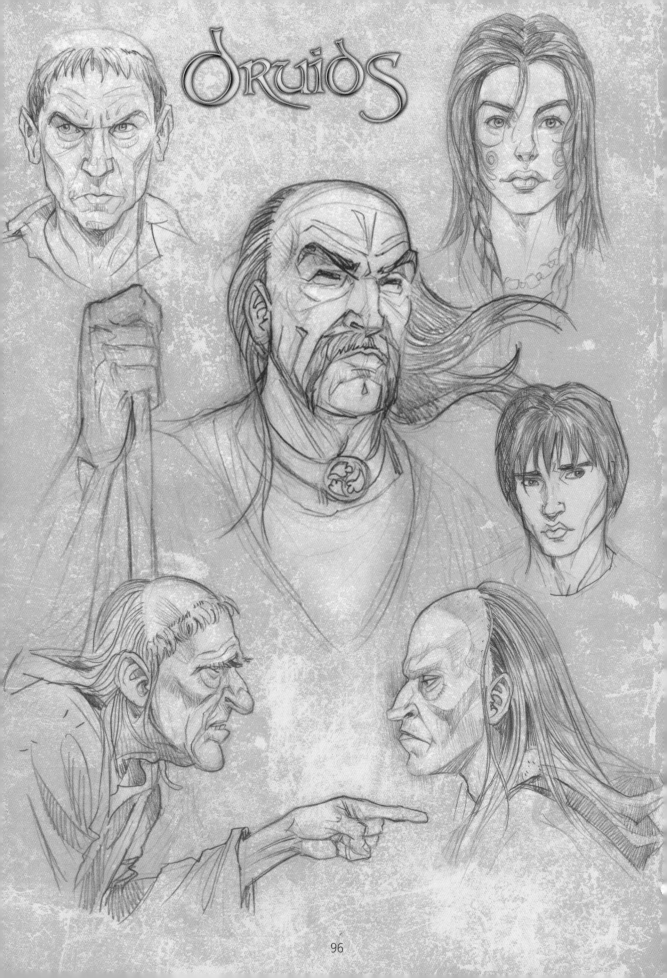

DRUIDS